D0783525

This igloo book belongs to:

Jamie Acrynh

igloobooks

Published in 2015
by Igloo Books Ltd
Cottage Farm
Sywell
NN6 0BJ
www.igloobooks.com

No part of this publication may be reproduced, stored in a retrieval system, or transmitted in any way
or by any means, electronic, mechanical, photocopying, recording or otherwise, without the prior
written permission of the publisher.

DreamWorks Dragons: Riders of Berk © 2014 DreamWorks Animation LLC.

HUN001 0215
2 4 6 8 10 9 7 5 3
ISBN: 978-1-78343-598-2

Printed and manufactured in China

DRAGONS
RIDERS OF BERK

igloobooks

Hiccup

Hiccup is the smartest, fastest and best Dragon Rider in the group. He is loyal, clever and compassionate and uses his head to overcome any problem that he faces. Hiccup is very good at inventing things and designed a new tail fin for his dragon, Toothless, when he was injured. Soon after, Hiccup was injured fighting against the Red Death. Gobber, the village blacksmith, made him a new prosthetic leg.

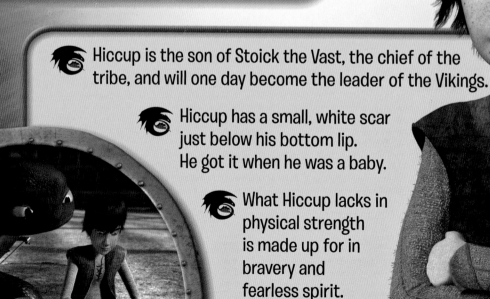

Hiccup is the son of Stoick the Vast, the chief of the tribe, and will one day become the leader of the Vikings.

Hiccup has a small, white scar just below his bottom lip. He got it when he was a baby.

What Hiccup lacks in physical strength is made up for in bravery and fearless spirit.

Toothless is a Night Fury dragon. They are the rarest of all the dragons. Toothless has incredible speed and super-strong fighting power. His signature move is to dive down through the air and shoot an extremely accurate plasma blast. Toothless is also a fantastic swimmer and can fly for the longest out of all the dragons, even when he is carrying extra weight.

Toothless

- Toothless is the fastest flying dragon on record.

- Toothless is Hiccup's best friend. They are even the same age.

- Toothless has the ability to guide himself using echolocation.

Astrid

Astrid is a very determined young woman. She is generally uninterested in other teenagers and prefers to study and practise dragon training skills to become a strong Viking warrior. Astrid is the second best Dragon Rider (after Hiccup). Her strong relationship with her dragon, Stormfly, means that they work very well together as a team.

- Astrid is very acrobatic and can perform handstands on top of Stormfly... while she is flying!

- Astrid is as brave as she is beautiful.

- Astrid is the Dragon Training Academy's Sharp Class Dragon expert.

Stormfly is a Deadly Nadder dragon. She is a very beautiful dragon and she knows it! Stormfly is very strong-willed and loyal to her rider, Astrid, and can be very protective when she needs to be. Deadly Nadder dragons do have a temper and, when needed, Stormfly can shoot spikes from her tail and breathe large streams of extremely hot fire.

Stormfly

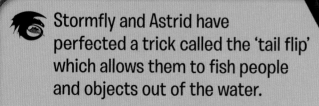 Stormfly and Astrid have perfected a trick called the 'tail flip' which allows them to fish people and objects out of the water.

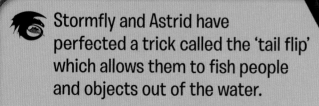 Stormfly can be agile, speedy and elegant when flying.

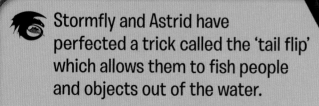 The food Stormfly likes best is chicken.

FISHLEGS

Fishlegs is a very intelligent Viking and has lots of useful dragon knowledge. Unlike Hiccup, who taught him how to ride a dragon, Fishlegs prefers to learn from books rather than experience. Fishlegs and his dragon, Meatlug, share a very affectionate relationship. Fishlegs refers to himself as 'Daddy' when speaking to her and the two like to play Toss the Sheep together. Meatlug also likes to lick Fishleg's feet before they go to sleep! They find it hard being away from one another.

Although he's very strong, Fishlegs is also one of the quietest members of the Dragon Training Academy.

Fishlegs is constantly adding to his vast knowledge of dragons. His ability to remember important facts has often saved the day.

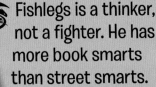

Fishlegs is a thinker, not a fighter. He has more book smarts than street smarts.

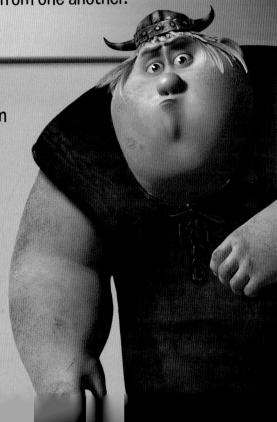

Meatlug is a Gronckle dragon. She is very sweet and sensitive compared to other dragon species. Meatlug can fly not only forward, but also backwards, up and down. She and Fishlegs have a very close relationship and Fishlegs is very protective of her. Like all Gronckle dragons, Meatlug eats rocks which allows her to breathe fire in the form of molten lava balls.

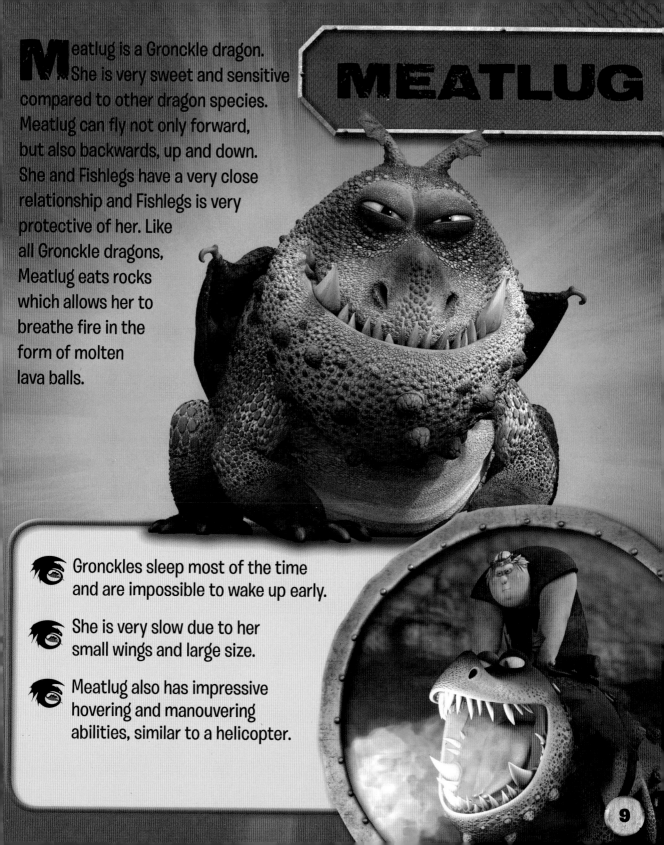

MEATLUG

- Gronckles sleep most of the time and are impossible to wake up early.

- She is very slow due to her small wings and large size.

- Meatlug also has impressive hovering and manouvering abilities, similar to a helicopter.

Ruffnut & Tuffnut

Ruffnut and Tuffnut are a brother and sister team. These twins often argue and squabble, but when they are in battle, they always protect each other. Both are skilled fighters and will often quarrel with each other. They understand each other's thoughts and ideas without speaking and often finish each other's sentences.

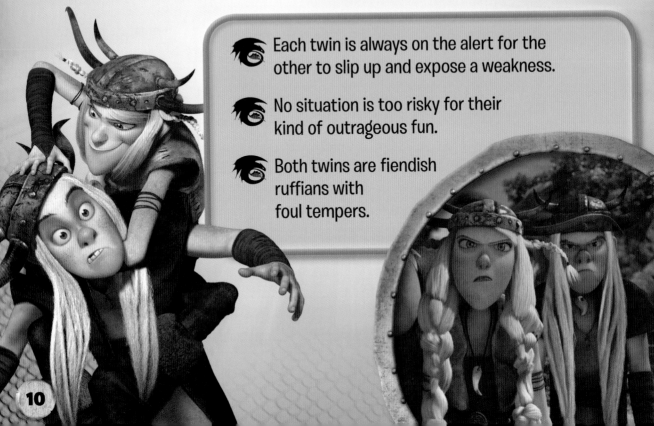

Each twin is always on the alert for the other to slip up and expose a weakness.

No situation is too risky for their kind of outrageous fun.

Both twins are fiendish ruffians with foul tempers.

Barf & Belch

Barf and Belch are a two headed Hideous Zippleback dragon. They have two heads that think differently and often disagree with each other, much like their Riders, Ruffnut and Tuffnut. Barf can breathe a toxic gas and Belch can produce a spark to ignite the gas to create an explosion.

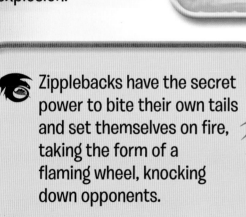

Zipplebacks have the secret power to bite their own tails and set themselves on fire, taking the form of a flaming wheel, knocking down opponents.

Barf and Belch are very agile, but sometimes get their necks tangled up!

Barf can let out a thick, green gas to help them to evade capture or attack.

Snotlout

Snotlout is a stubborn and often quite selfish member of the team. He likes to think that he is the best at Dragon Riding and fighting, but he isn't. Though extremely tough and determined, Snotlout envies Hiccup's skills and intelligence, but he'll never admit it. His hidden sensitivity shows when his dragon, Hookfang, is in danger.

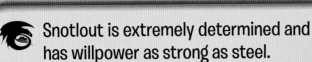 Snotlout is extremely determined and has willpower as strong as steel.

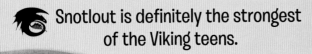 Snotlout is definitely the strongest of the Viking teens.

 Despite not studying up on dragons, Snotlout has discovered some effective manoeuvres with his dragon, Hookfang.

ookfang is a Monstrous Nightmare dragon. Like his Rider, Snotlout, Monstrous Nightmare dragons are strong and can be hot-headed. When provoked, Hookfang can coat his body in a flammable gel and ignite it. Hookfang likes to make Snotlout scream and often does crazy moves when flying to playfully terrify him.

Hookfang

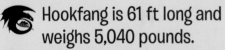 Hookfang is 61 ft long and weighs 5,040 pounds.

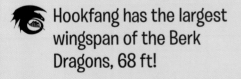 Hookfang has the largest wingspan of the Berk Dragons, 68 ft!

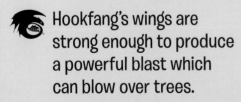 Hookfang's wings are strong enough to produce a powerful blast which can blow over trees.

In the village of Berk, there was trouble between the dragons and the Vikings. The dragons were causing chaos around the village. They ate all the Vikings' food, stole supplies and damaged everything as they flew around. The Vikings were fed up.

"What use are these dragons!" cried Mildew, a grumpy old Viking. "They just make a mess and eat all of our food." The leader of the villagers, Stoick, agreed. He ordered his son, Hiccup, to take the dragons and lock them up in cages. Hiccup was sad. He loved dragons, especially his own, a Night Fury called Toothless.

Continued on page 18

WHAT A MESS!

The Dragon Riders and villagers of Berk cannot believe the mess that the dragons are making. Can you help them to find all the items listed?

Answer on page 24

16

Things to find

1 Chest

2 Books

3 Barrels

4 Terrible
Terrors

5 Axes

6 Shields

Hiccup and his friends, Astrid, Snotlout, Fishlegs, Ruffnut and Tuffnut
walked their dragons toward the cages. They didn't want them
to be locked up. Suddenly, Hiccup had an idea. "That's it!" he cried.
"If we train the dragons to help us, my father will have to let us keep them."
His friends all agreed and after a sucessful training session, they flew
off on their dragons to help the Vikings around Berk.

As they flew over a fishing boat in Berk Harbour, Snotlout and
his dragon, Hookfang, dived down into the sea. A second later, they shot
out of the water surrounded by terrified fish which jumped into the
fishermen's nets. Then, the dragons flew over the fields and herded
all the animals. With the dragons' help, doing chores in the village
was now much easier.

Continued on page 22

MAZE RUN

Hiccup has had an idea. Help him to race to
save his friends by finding the correct
path through the Village of Berk.

START

FINISH

Answer
on page 24

FISH FRENZY

Hookfang has dived into the sea to scare all the fish. Take it in turns to close your eyes and try to hit the targets with your finger. Every time you do, give yourself a point. The first player to hit all the targets wins!

As they finished helping to plough the fields using the dragons' spiky tails, Stoick called for Hiccup and his friends. Hiccup was worried. He thought that they were going to get into trouble, but when the six friends met Stoick, he was smiling. "Hiccup, your courage and quick thinking has saved the village. I'm proud of you," said Stoick.

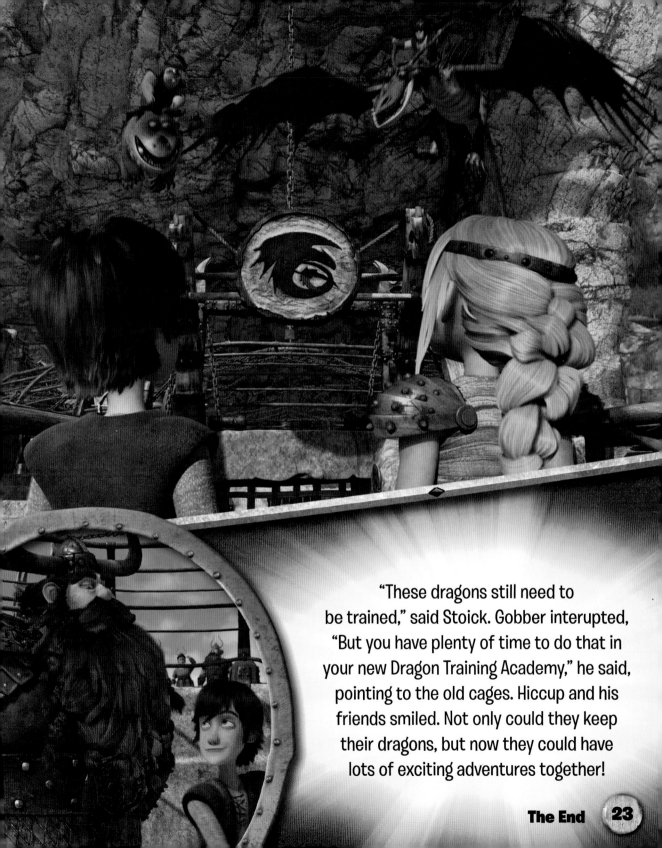

"These dragons still need to be trained," said Stoick. Gobber interupted, "But you have plenty of time to do that in your new Dragon Training Academy," he said, pointing to the old cages. Hiccup and his friends smiled. Not only could they keep their dragons, but now they could have lots of exciting adventures together!

The End

ANSWERS

MAZE RUN

WHAT A MESS!